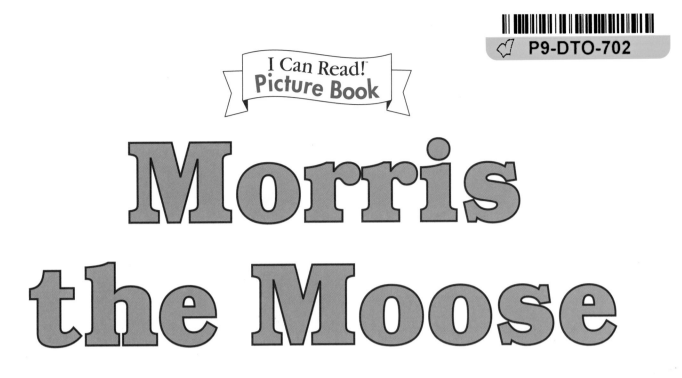

Morris the Moose

by B. Wiseman

BARNES & NOBLE

NEW YORK

For Barbara Dicks

One day

Morris the Moose

saw a cow.

"You are

a funny-looking moose,"

he said.

"I am a COW.

I am not a MOOSE!"

said the cow.

"You have four legs

and a tail

and things on your head,"

said Morris.

"You are a moose."

"But I say MOO!"

said the cow.

"I can say MOO too!"

said Morris.

The cow said,

"I give MILK to people."

"So you are a moose
who gives milk to people!"
said Morris.

"But my mother

is a COW!"

said the cow.

"You are a MOOSE,"

said Morris.

"So your mother

must be a moose too!"

"What can I tell you?"

the cow said.

"You can tell me

you are a moose,"

said Morris.

14

"No!" cried the cow.

"I am NOT a moose!

Ask him.

He will tell you

what I am."

15

"What is she?"

Morris asked the deer.

The deer said,

"She has four legs

and a tail

and things on her head.

She is a deer, like me."

"She is a MOOSE, like ME!"

Morris yelled.

"You?

You are not a moose.

You are a deer too!"

The deer laughed.

"I am a MOOSE!"

cried Morris.

"You are a DEER!"

shouted the deer.

"What can I tell you?"

asked Morris.

"You can tell me

you are a deer,"

said the deer.

21

"Let's ask
somebody else,"
said the cow.

"Okay, Moose," said Morris the Moose.

"Okay, Deer," said the deer.

They walked until

they found a horse.

"Hello, you horses!"

said the horse.

"What are those funny things

on your heads?"

"Oh, dear." The cow sighed.

"Let's ask somebody else.

But first, let's get a drink."

Morris, the cow, and the deer

drank from a cool, blue stream.

Morris looked at himself

in the water and smiled.

"You two do not look

at all like me," he said.

"You cannot be moose."

28

"You mean,
you are not DEER,"
said the deer.
"You don't look
at all like me."

"See?" said the cow.

"I am not a moose

or a deer.

I am a COW!

You made a MISTAKE."

"I did not," said Morris.

"I made a MOOSEtake!"